FOREST LANDSCAPE DESIGN GUIDELINES

FOREWORD

It is nearly 30 years since Dame Sylvia Crowe first gave advice to foresters about the visual effects of forests upon the landscape.

The principles of forest design are well established within the Forestry Commission to the extent that carefully defined techniques in the management of a complete range of woodland types in relation to landform are currently practised.

The need, and indeed vision, of a better landscape is central to that quest of both foresters and a wider public who use and enjoy forests.

These guidelines, prepared by the Forestry Commission's landscape architects, will enable a practical and realistic message on design to be more widely heard and understood to the benefit of the countryside as a whole.

GORDON PATTERSON
Landscape Consultant to
the Forestry Commission

FOREST
LANDSCAPE
DESIGN

GUIDELINES

LONDON : HMSO

ISBN 0 11 710325 X

Printed in the United Kingdom for HMSO

Dd 294489 C40 3/94

Enquiries relating to this publication should be addressed to:

The Research Publications Officer
The Forestry Authority
Research Division
Alice Holt Lodge
Wrecclesham
Farnham
Surrey
GU10 4LH

FOREST LANDSCAPE DESIGN GUIDELINES

INTRODUCTION

Landscape is affected by uses of land which determine the pattern of vegetation. The greatest contrast is between trees and open ground, and the major landscape changes in our times have been brought about by the creation of woods and forests, particularly in the uplands.

With the continuing expansion of woodland, it is important to maintain the qualities of naturalness in the landscape. People's natural dislike of alteration to familiar surroundings will cause them to view these changes critically. Forests and woods must meet the needs of society by producing timber, creating varied and extensive wildlife habitats, and providing recreational opportunities for people to enjoy. Woodland must also look attractive and be seen to be in harmony with the rest of the countryside.

These guidelines are intended to provide applicants for the Woodland Grant Scheme and applicants for felling licences with an outline of the principles and practical applications of forest design. They represent the basic standard which will be expected in any application for grant aid in the generally more upland areas of Britain. Guidance on the design of lowland landscapes and community woodlands are covered by other Forestry Commission publications. They do not attempt to cover every aspect of landscape design or details of design techniques. Applicants should be aware of the importance of landscape in all aspects of forest planning and forest operations, and of the need to achieve a high standard of design, particularly in sensitive landscapes. The guidelines indicate what they should look out for, and situations which need special attention. Landscape design is a complex subject and professional help from qualified landscape architects may be needed in certain situations.

There are certain areas where an existing open landscape is of outstanding quality. Here the relative values of open land and forestry must be most carefully assessed. The characteristic qualities must be identified and a measure established of how extensively they occur locally and elsewhere. Good design may be able to resolve possible conflicts between such characteristic qualities of the landscape and the changes likely to result from the establishment of new woodlands. *If this is not possible, planting should not take place in these areas.*

Comprehensive landscape plans are necessary when new planting is undertaken on a substantial scale or when extensive felling is planned. The patterns established at these times may persist for half a century.

DESIGN PRINCIPLES

Forest landscape design depends upon an appreciation of six key design principles. These are shape, scale, diversity, visual force, unity, and 'the spirit of the place'.

Shape

Shape has a powerful and evocative effect on how we see our surroundings. Appropriate shapes are essential as they dominate other design factors. Good scale, diversity and so on will not rescue a design if shape is wrong because the mind is quick to pick out incongruities and artificial geometric qualities. Compatible shapes are vital for the overall unity of the landscape.

The perception of shape is influenced by overall proportions, viewing position and direction, and the nature of the external boundary edge. Diagonal shapes have a most pleasing effect. Lines at right angles to the contour rarely look pleasing because the proportions of landscape are broadly horizontal. The distinction between natural and geometric shapes is specially significant and plays a major part in forest landscape design.

1a and b. Geometric shapes such as squares and rectangles contradict the shape of the landform and the vegetation patterns (above) whereas the natural, irregular shapes in the forest (below) reflect the shapes contained in the landform.

Visual Force

Visual force is a principle which is embodied in art, graphic design and architecture. The eye and the mind respond to visual force in a predictable and dynamic way. The visual forces in landform draw the eye down convex slopes and up concave ones, the strength of the visual force depending on the scale and irregularity of the landform.

Forest shapes should be designed to follow visual forces in landform by rising up in hollows and falling on spurs and ridges to create a well-unified relationship between the two. The pattern of natural vegetation is often similar, with plants from lower ground tending to continue higher in sheltered hollows than on exposed ridges. Forest shapes which reflect such patterns tend to match up with expectations of what a natural landscape looks like. If the shape of a block of woodland or a felling area conflicts with the visual forces in the landscape it will look disruptive and out of place.

2. The circle appears to be pushing against the black and white stripes and distorting them, giving a strong sense of movement across the image.

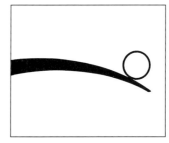 

3. The illustrations suggest a bending downwards and rolling to the right and then an upward bounce.

4a. Llyn Brianne, Dyfed.

5a. A landscape in Northumberland.

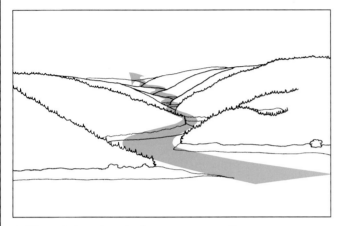

b. The eye is drawn bouncing from one spur to another.

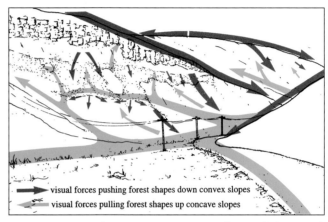

→ visual forces pushing forest shapes down convex slopes
→ visual forces pulling forest shapes up concave slopes

b. Analysis of visual forces. The strongest arrows illustrate the largest and most pronounced forms, the smallest the more subtle shapes.

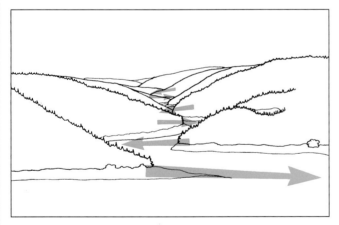

c. The spurs appear drawn together, each into the bay opposite.

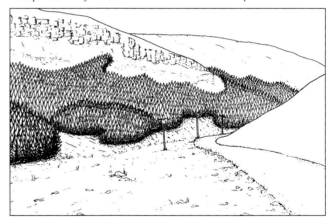

c. The forest margin shapes responding to the visual forces creating a direct relationship between the forest cover and the landscape.

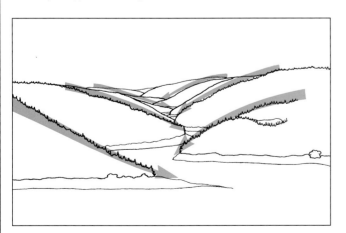

d. The eye is drawn downwards on the spurs.

6. The effect of visual forces can be seen in this example at Ratagan where effects of grazing and burning have restricted the woodland to the lower slopes and valleys.

Scale

Scale is a matter of relative and absolute size and has a major effect on perception. The scale of a forest or woodland should reflect the scale of the landscape. Much depends on the location of the viewpoint. The scale of a landscape increases the further you can see, the wider the unrestricted view, and the greater the elevation of the observer. The scale of landscape is thus greater on higher slopes and hill tops than on lower slopes and in valleys. Areas appear to be of different size when seen from different points. Small shapes may appear to be out of scale when viewed from a distance in a large scale landscape.

It follows that as the scale of the landscape changes, so should the scale of the forest and woodland shapes, with gradual change from one area to another. When a landscape is seen as being divided into different parts, a ratio of one-third to two-thirds is often the most satisfying. A hillside which appears to be one-third open land and two-thirds wooded or the converse looks more pleasing than a proportion of half-and-half which produces a feeling of unnatural symmetry.

7. A small scale landscape where close up views of fine detail are apparent.

8. Trees and forest edges defining the scale of the landscape. If the edge is too far away, control of the scale may be lost.

9. A very large scale landscape where the forest is seen as one element along with the water, mountains and semi-natural vegetation. The proportion of species and felling areas should relate to the large scale. Small areas would appear fussy in such a landscape.

10a. Ennerdale, Lake District viewed from Green Gable.

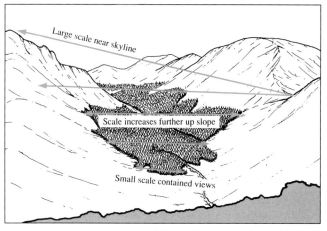

b. Large scale landscape near the skyline with smaller scale in the valley bottom. The change of scale from one part of the landscape to another should take place gradually and abrupt changes avoided.

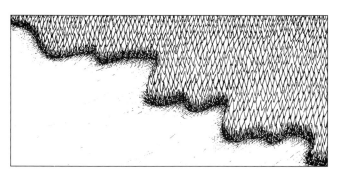

11a. The effect of scale and distance in the variation in shape along a woodland edge looks quite interesting . . .

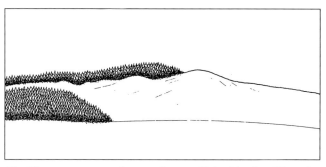

12a. The open space occupies more than two-thirds of the view. The scale of the upper remnant of forest is too small and the composition looks unbalanced.

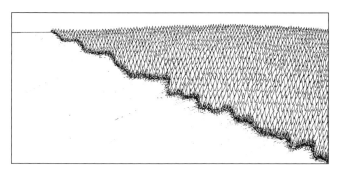

b. . . . yet from a viewpoint further away the overall impression is of a straight line with a few small-scale variations along it.

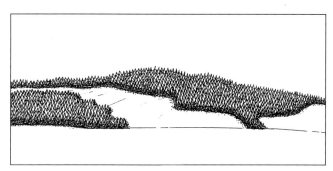

b. Proportions on a roughly one-third to two-thirds basis produces a far more comfortable scale.

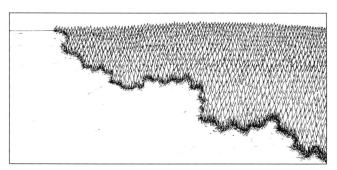

c. The edge should be designed to look right from the further distance before the detail shaping suitable for closer views.

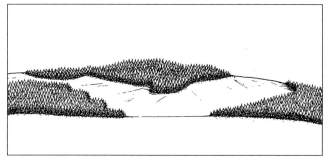

c. Nearly equal amounts of forest and open space produce a far less resolved result.

Diversity

Diversity is the number and degree of different features in a landscape or design. Diversity is a treasured feature of British landscape as a result of varied geology, climate and the long history of human settlement and land use. Landscape diversity is linked to ecological diversity, but the two are distinct and not necessarily equivalent.

Woods and forest introduce diversity into treeless landscapes, but newly-created young woodland, whether broadleaved or conifer, can reduce diversity if it hides landscape detail. We should take the opportunity to create diversity in otherwise uniform landscape, but it should not be overdone. Excessive diversity often leads to a restless confusion in a landscape design.

Increased diversity often has the effect of reducing scale and can be used to do so where some reduction in scale is desirable. A high level of diversity is acceptable if one element is clearly dominant. For example, one species might occupy two-thirds of a wood with the remaining third consisting of a diversity of different species.

13. Diverse landscape of Strathtay, Perthshire.

Unity

Unity is the essential object of landscape design and can be achieved in a number of ways.

Landform has a major influence on landscape character, and woods and forests should be designed in relation to it. This can be done by using shape, visual force and scale to unite the woodland with the landscape and to counterbalance contrasts of colour, texture and form.

The large scale of woodland means that it has to be designed to blend rather than contrast with the landscape. Even-aged forest tends to be highly unified and lacking in diversity, while contrasting strongly with open ground beyond it, through darker colour, stronger shadows, coarser texture and the vertical height of the trees. These contrasts are overcome by designing shapes, external margins, open space within the forest and the pattern of species, so that shapes interlock and unite the forest within the surrounding landscape.

14. A pattern of natural elements well unified in the landscape. Here the forest area follows the landform, being related to drainage pattern. The location of shelter and soil, rock outcrops and climatic factors has resulted in the surface pattern being strongly related to landform. Analysis of visual forces would show that the forest is predominantly related to the valleys and hollows while the spurs are free of trees.

'The Spirit of the Place'

'The spirit of the place'. When these design principles are satisfied there will remain something unique to a particular place which is an important asset and stimulus to good design and which should be conserved and if possible enhanced. It is often expressed by particular contrasts or combinations of features. Forest design should ensure that these features are emphasised, not hidden. Enclosed valleys, or very exposed summits or high points; indications of great antiquity, such as old trees and rocks; places where the lighting is dramatic, especially when associated with water; all these contribute to a powerful sense of place, particularly where there is a feeling of wildness.

This aspect of landscape design is elusive and easier to conserve where it already exists than to create. The features and qualities which contribute to it should be recognised and incorporated in the designs for individual sites.

15. The dramatic gorge and waterfall at Corrieshalloch together with precarious trees and flying spray produce a strong spirit of place which should be protected.

APPRAISAL OF THE LANDSCAPE

Landscape design must accommodate the many functions of a forest and do so cost-effectively. A design can only be truly satisfactory if it is functional. The design process is the method by which all the site constraints and functional aspects are reconciled with visual and other environmental considerations. It begins with an assessment of the existing landscape. Some aspects are general and not easy to define precisely. The following factors should be carefully assessed before design work starts.

Sensitivity

The sensitivity of a landscape depends on its resilience in relation to change. This can be a subjective judgement. Landscape sensitivity is also a function of its visibility and the number of people who see it, either as residents or visitors. The most valuable landscapes often tend to be the most sensitive because their precise character is what is valued most highly. The highest quality landscapes in the main lie within the areas of statutory landscape designation, such as National Parks, Areas of Outstanding Natural Beauty and National Scenic Areas.

Character

Character is a distinct pattern of elements which occur consistently in a particular type or landscape. A landscape may have a desirable or undesirable character. By recognising character it is easier to assess whether it will be altered significantly by land use changes, such as the establishment of woodland. The elements which distinguish character may be natural (landform, vegetation), human (field patterns, settlements, buildings), or aesthetic (shape, scale, colour).

Heritage

Landscapes are valued for their historic and traditional associations as well as for their aesthetic qualities. Heritage is an important factor particularly when the landscape has not changed in historic times.

Elements of Diversity

Elements of diversity include landform, water, rocks and crags; wildlife, both plant and animal; and special areas such as archaeological sites, recreational areas and impressive viewpoints. These should be protected and planting kept well away from them. Design in relation to these areas needs special treatment. As far as the forest is concerned diversity can be achieved internally by the use of contrasting species, particularly deciduous and evergreen and by making use of unplanted open spaces.

Special Features

Distinctive features stand out from the general background or context, and landscape changes near a dominant feature should be carefully designed to maintain or emphasise its character. Significant rock outcrops, well known landmarks or focal views are some examples of identifiable features. Changes are more easily made in less dominant parts of the landscape, where they will blend less obtrusively since the eye will concentrate on the special feature or features.

APPLYING DESIGN PRINCIPLES TO WOODLAND LANDSCAPES

Good woodland and forest design requires the correct application of the principles outlined in the first section.

Woodland Shapes

Successful woodland landscape design depends more on the creation of naturalistic shapes than on any other factor. The shapes are those of whole blocks of forest, entire woods, external margins, open spaces and felling areas. They should be similar to those in the surrounding landscape and should follow landform.

    Each shape interacts with its neighbours, and the general design of a shape should be resolved before considering details of line or edge treatments.

Woodland shapes should:

- have gently curved edges. These are always better than straight lines. Where a ragged edge is desired, it will always be more effective if superimposed on a curved shape;

- be diagonal in emphasis; nearer horizontal in flatter country, more strongly diagonal on steep hillsides;

- relate to landform, with high points positioned in main hollows or gullies and low points on or near to prominent spurs of ridges;

- borrow from the shapes in the surrounding landscape smoothly rounded, irregular, ragged-edged, as appropriate;

- avoid regularity and symmetry, by moving 'peaks' or 'troughs' so that they are slightly offset. A good contour map, accurately marked with the visual forces in terms of size, strength and direction, is a great help;

- be interlocked as far as possible, whether they are shapes of open ground and woodland or of different species. This is most important in achieving good integration of shapes into a unified landscape design.

16a. A landscape of rounded landforms.

b. The forest layout should respond with flowing, curved shapes to pick up the character and emphasise the forms.

17a. A landscape of broken rugged landforms.

b. The forest layout is jagged and spikey, picking up the rock outcrops.

18. Geometric rides and larch shapes stand out strongly.

Improving Poor Designs

It is often necessary to improve the design of existing woodland. This can be done most readily and cheaply when the woods are young, particularly in the first 20 years. Attempts to improve design in mid-rotation may increase the risk of windthrow as well as being more costly. Under the Woodland Grant Scheme the management grants may be used to improve the design of existing plantations.

The quality of existing forest shapes can be improved substantially by eliminating:

- right angles;

- straight edges at right angles to the contours, or nearly so;

- edges following contours;

- parallel sides or parallel lines; existing belts are best treated by partial clearance to create irregularity spaced groups of varying size;

- symmetrical shapes;

- long straight edges.

Straight lines are least objectionable where they are short and diagonal to the contour; at lower margins of the woodland where they reflect valley field patterns; and in flat landscapes where the fields are already geometric in shape. The scale of the forest may need to be improved by removing trees or by additional planting. Open spaces may be opened which will provide added diversity, some planted with broadleaves. The opportunity may also be taken to establish the boundaries of eventual felling coupes by felling swathes or "severance cuts" to enable green, stable edges to develop. This is particularly useful in areas prone to windthrow. The severance cuts should be variable in width and incorporate groups of broadleaves at various points.

19a. An existing plantation of very poor design - geometric in shape, low in diversity and failing to be unified with its surroundings.

b. A possible solution which involves felling but not replanting in order to create better external margins and internal open space together with more diversity of species. Ideally extra land needs to be planted to be able to correct the design fully.

Upper Margins

The shaping and location of the woodland boundary requires rigorous application of the principles of shape, scale, diversity and unity in order to blend the woodland into the landscape. It is here that the contrasts of colour and texture between forest and open ground are most acute.

The upper margin is usually the most prominent. It should:

- rise uphill in hollows and fall on convex ground and spurs;

- reflect the quality of the landform - jagged in rugged country and smooth in smooth topography;

- be placed so that any open ground below the crest is of sufficient size to reflect the scale of the hill cap or ridge. Avoid narrow slivers between the forest and the skyline; a completely planted skyline is often preferable;

- be irregularly shaped with a generally diagonal alignment. This is not easy. There is always a tendency to create horizontal lines, which must be recognised and resisted.

20a. In this example the upper margin follows the contour.

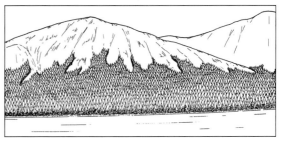

b. The rugged terrain suggests a much more broken, spikey margin to express the quality of the landform.

Skylines

The prominence and sensitivity of the upper margin is at its most acute at the skyline as seen from the main viewpoints. It is best to avoid narrow strips close to the skyline, whether of open ground, woodland, contrasting ages or species. Keep the skyline substantially forested or largely open, and avoid diffuse belts, retained fringes and groups or scattered trees.

Boundaries between contrasting areas, such as the edges of felling coupes, different species or forest margins, should cross the skyline as close to low points as possible, and away from summits and convexities. All margins should cross the skyline diagonally and on a curved alignment.

Group fellings on skylines often give small-scale effects which look quite out of place. Avoid them. Scale is larger higher up the hill, and skylines must have sufficiently sized felling areas.

The serrated outline of most conifers can be inappropriate on a skyline in predominantly broadleaved woodland. Consider using pines (particularly Scots pine) on sensitive skylines where their more rounded crowns achieve a better unity with the broadleaved trees.

21a. The upper edge of the forest is too near the skyline and does not follow landform properly. The rounded topography suggests that flowing shapes should be adopted.

b. Extending planting to the skyline removes the narrow strip of open ground but reduces diversity.

c. A more flowing, diagonal, upper margin positioned lower down the slope improves the scale of the open space.

22. A prominent skyline in a predominantly broadleaved landscape with conifers on the skyline. The rounded crowns of Scots pine would create stronger links with the broadleaved character of the hedgerows.

23. A fringe left on the skyline after felling is badly out of scale. The retained cap should obey thirds rule in order to work at this scale.

Side Margins

In some landscapes there may be a strong pattern of hedgerows or walls or dykes extending up the slope and often forming the boundary of the woodland. Straight side margins can be acceptable here, provided that they change direction at a similar scale to the walls or hedgerows. Otherwise side margins look best in the form of gently curving diagonals, varied appropriately in hollows, (with the woodland below, not above the diagonal). Avoid straight vertical edges.

Woodland should have a logical place to stop, such as a stream, crag or a depression. If there is no obvious natural feature, emphasise the limit of the wooded area by a group of contrasting species, especially broadleaves.

24a. Darling How, Thornthwaite Forest. An intrusive side margin in a sensitive landscape.

b. Improved design, possible if additional land can be planted on the lower slope. Felling into the existing forest is necessary to avoid the straight line showing as a distinct age difference.

Lower Margins

Though these are less prominent, they are often seen in closer view and small scale variation is important. If fields below have a strong hedgerow pattern it is acceptable to reflect this in a geometric layout, though rectangular shapes should not extend into the forest. Links with the hedgerows should be strengthened by extending broadleaves into conifer woodland, especially up hollows and gullies.

Where there is little or no hedgerow pattern, adopt a lower margin of diagonally curving lines, rising in hollows, falling on spurs. Existing long straight margins should be realigned, and should not follow contours.

25. In this Devon landscape the lower front margin blends with the strong enclosure pattern. The hedgerow broadleaves extend into the forest up a gully, creating stronger links between the two land uses.

26. The sweeping curves of the lower margin respond to the landform in the landscape where there are no strong enclosure patterns.

Edges

Though woodland edges and margins are the same physically, in design terms they are distinct. The margin defines the shape of a space, whereas the edge is a matter of individual elements of individual trees and small groups of trees. The edge detail is usually superimposed on a previously designed margin such as a wall, hedge or fence. Although external edges are the most obvious, the same detailed treatment should be applied to edges within the forest, wherever trees adjoin more or less open ground.

The shape of the forest margin must be attractive, and completely designed before details of edge treatment are worked out. Edges, no matter how well designed, will not improve bad shapes.

Where there is no existing pattern of trees in the surrounding landscape, the edge should reflect landform or the pattern of ground vegetation. These are useful pointers in the gradual changes from woodland to open ground in natural forest.

Natural forest edges feature:

- decreasing density of trees;

- strong indentations;

- decreasing size of tree groups;

- increasing spacing between groups and individual trees;

- decreasing height of individual trees; more shrubby species;

- increasing presence of species more typical of open habitat.

In man-made woodlands the edges should be made to look as natural as practicable and varied in scale with the landscape:

- By detailed shaping of the edge. The protrusions and indentations of the main mass of the woodland are important visual links and should follow landform in the same way as woodland shapes. They should be irregular in size and distribution to avoid unnatural symmetry.

27. A natural upper edge on Hudson's Bay Mountain in British Columbia, Canada, shows the typical features – decreasing density and size of tree groups.

28. Looking towards natural Shore pine forest from an open bog. The decline in tree size on the edge of the bog emphasises the natural quality of the edge. Pacific Rim National Park, British Columbia.

Conifer

Thinned conifer

Broadleaves

Areas to be planted later to give age diversity

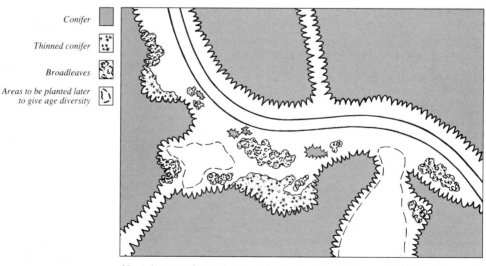

29. A diagram of a good and bad forest edge. The sketch shows the different elements that go to make up the better design.

- By using species with different growth rates to vary tree height on the edge. This avoids a continuous wall effect, particularly with conifers. Creation of tapered edges by the use of transitions from fast-growing conifers, through slower conifers and broadleaves to shrubs. This should be done in appropriate places, for example along roadsides, or where edges cross prominent skylines or ridges.

- By extending tree spacing towards the edge of the wood. Wider spacing should be irregular, particularly in small-scale landscapes, or close to roads, regular spacing looks artificial, treatment must be bold if it is not to be visually insignificant.

- By establishing irregular outlying groups. These should be near enough to the woodland to be seen as part of it, not 'free-floating', and positioned so as to seem to be a natural extension. Avoid too many groups, which will make the scale too small and appear too regular.

- By planting individual trees close to the forest edge or outlying groups, to link up the woodland with open ground. Give them room to develop well-shaped crowns.

- By thinning to create a softer edge to felling areas, allowing the opening to penetrate into the adjoining stands. This can be enhanced in sensitive areas by pruning dead branches to varying height and so lessening the 'brown edge' effect.

The opportunity to establish ecologically and visually diverse edges at time of planting should not be missed. It is cheaper to do it then and the results will be better, particularly where edges cannot be thinned later because of risk of windthrow. The wildlife value of edges is greater than the values of the interior; good landscape design of edges can contribute to this by creating a diversity of field, shrub, understorey and canopy layers in various combinations. Variation in conditions of light and moisture provided by different ages, species and densities of trees in an irregular edge can greatly increase the wildlife value of woodland – and it looks much more interesting.

30. This upper edge in a planted forest has been eroded by scree and resembles a natural upper edge. Care is needed, however, to ensure that the overall margin shape is designed before this detail is encouraged.

31. An edge where pine and broadleaves of varying size and spacing grades the forest edge down to the field boundary.

Open Space in the Forest

Open space is of great value for visual and ecological diversity, and as a means of controlling the scale of woodland landscape. This is specially important in very extensive upland forests where diversity of species is difficult to achieve.

The design of open space depends on whether it is seen in long view from outside, or from inside the forest. In long view it appears as another shape, while internal views see it in terms of open space.

Farmland within a forest may echo patterns of fields and enclosures outside the forest. Where the forest is surrounded by open moorland, more irregular shapes following the landform are better.

Linear spaces are usually man-made and include rides, roads and power lines. They tend to split the forest and to destroy the unity of the wooded landscape. Where they run near to the forest edge it is usually better to keep the intervening area open, rather than have narrow strips of forest.

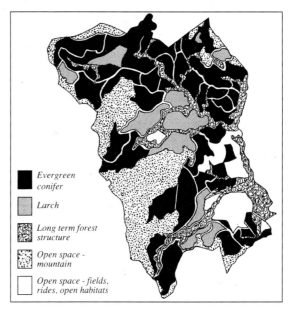

■ Evergreen conifer

▨ Larch

▦ Long term forest structure

▨ Open space - mountain

□ Open space - fields, rides, open habitats

32. This diagram shows the interrelationships between the various types of open space in the forest.

Rides

Rides are unsurfaced access routes and are also used to mark compartments. Modern practice is to plan road systems at a very early stage and to make use of roads, streams, crags and other natural features as compartment boundaries. The earlier practice of leaving wide swathes unplanted to form firebreaks has been superseded by good access road systems. The old geometric ride systems and many of the firebreaks are often grossly artificial and visually intrusive. These visual eyesores need to be planted or otherwise modified to blend in with the rest of the forest.

The layout of rides should be designed to reflect landform. Width, shape and direction should be varied, and long straight stretches - daunting to walkers - should be avoided. Rides are often important as wildlife habitat and special management measures can often improve their ecological value. In intensively managed farmland, woodland rides may contain the best remaining examples of relatively undisturbed grass-herb communities.

33. Long straight rides are daunting and unattractive to walkers.

34. The geometric rides and compartment boundaries add another layer of geometry to this plantation.

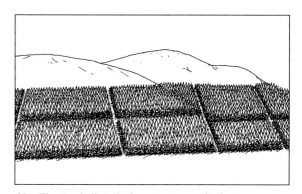

35a. The visual effect of rides set out perpendicular to or parallel with the contour is very intrusive.

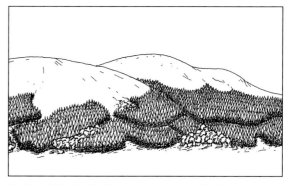

b. Rides following landform and connected with other open spaces such as rocky outcrops and streams look much less intrusive.

Forest Roads

Forest roads have similar design requirements to rides and should:

- be located to minimise visual impact, within the technical limitations of the harvesting road network;

- avoid, if possible, small scale landscapes with strong sense of place;

- be kept clear of archaeological sites and wildlife habitat of special importance;

- follow landform with variation in curve and gradient;

- cross skylines at the lowest practicable point;

- have cuttings and embankments which use natural form and allow re-establishment of vegetation;

- have turning points and landings located as far as possible where natural gradients provide space, and not positioned on prominent spurs or ridges.

Cuttings and soil can be particularly unsightly. In areas of soft rock, cuttings should be made with rounded banks, with tops sloped off to prevent the formation of overhanging turf. This, alienated by dark shadows underneath, makes an intrusive black line parallel to the road.

Cuts in harder rock should not have precisely even faces. Make strong irregular shapes instead, similar to natural rock outcrops. This also applies to borrow-pits and quarry faces.

On particularly prominent situations it may be necessary to re-establish vegetation on cuttings or fill. Sowing grass is only satisfactory if the surrounding vegetation is exactly the same colour. It is better to use clumps of natural vegetation obtained from turf and topsoil stripped from the site. It should not blanket the soil but be placed in irregular shapes, extending the natural vegetation and helping to integrate the road with the landscape through a series of interlocking shapes.

36a. A forest road which is well related to landform with plenty of variation in vertical and horizontal alignment.

b. A straight roadline produced by a precisely even gradient where there is no response to the strongly diagonal emphasis of this rocky landscape.

37. Cross section of forest road profile:

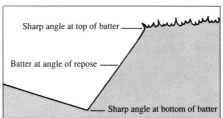

Sharp angle at top of batter

Batter at angle of repose

Sharp angle at bottom of batter

A precisely engineered profile ...

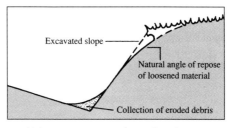

Excavated slope

Natural angle of repose of loosened material

Collection of eroded debris

... which soon starts to weather and erode ...

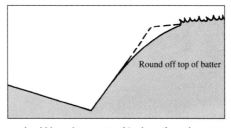

Round off top of batter

... should have been cut to this shape from the outset.

38. A small rock cutting has been worked into the surrounding landform. It will colonise with vegetation and blend easily into its surroundings.

Power Lines

Power lines are similar to rides in their visual effect. There are many instances where power lines have been deliberately routed through woodland with the misguided notion that this would hide them. The open wayleave corridor is often a greater visual affront than the towers carrying the line. Power lines should be planned to follow open space, and to run alongside, not through, woodland. It is up to Forest Managers and planning authorities to insist on this.

Where there really is no alternative route, a power line through the forest should:

- avoid areas of landscape sensitivity;

- not follow the line of sight of important views;

- be kept in valleys and depressions;

- not divide a hill into two similar parts where it crosses over a summit;

- cross skylines or ridges where they dip to a low point;

- follow alignments diagonal to the contour as far as possible;

- vary in the alignment to reflect the landform by rising in hollows and descending on ridges.

Within the forest the power line should seem to pass through a series of irregular spaces. The forest should appear to meet across the open space in some places so that the corridor does not split the forest completely. An even width of corridor is not obligatory because trees can be planted closer to the line opposite pylons than in mid-span, where the line hangs lower and swings more. Smaller trees and shrubs can be grown closer still, as an extension of the forest edge towards the power line. This edge should be designed to create irregular spaces with irregular tree heights, avoiding severe vertical edges, particularly of conifers. The aim should be a corridor of varying character and width, swinging from one side of the line to the other, taking care to avoid irregular but parallel edges, or irregular but symmetrical space. Exit points should be gently asymmetrical bell-mouths. Felling areas should be planned to link with and across the power line corridor and create greater irregularity.

Similar design considerations apply to pipelines and any other service corridors through the forest which need to be kept clear of trees.

39. Beattock Summit, Lanarkshire. This area is seen from the A74. The powerline corridor is very intrusive in the landscape, especially where it crosses the skyline.

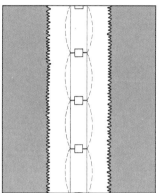 

40. The plan and section of a typical wayleave corridor showing the very intrusive geometric effect (above) which can be improved by varying the width and developing broadleaved planting, especially closer to the pylons (below).

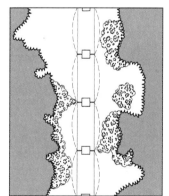 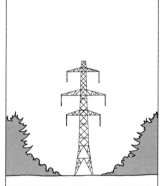

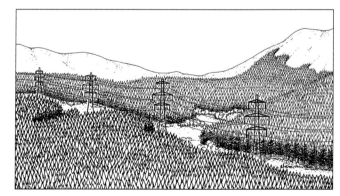

41. This sketch shows the powerline corridor well shaped to fit into the landscape. The edges appear to connect visually in places to break the linear effect. Other open spaces such as streams are also connected into the powerline corridor and help link it into the surrounding landscape better.

Streamsides

Streamsides should be maintained with adequate natural bankside vegetation to protect water quality and minimise erosion. Unplanted streamside buffer areas should be irregular, with the edges designed to link across the open space at key points. In a conifer forest continuous strips of streamside broadleaves can be as inappropriate as corridors of open ground. The aim should be to have an irregular distribution with about 50% of the stream in full sunlight, the rest receiving light dappled shade from broadleaves.

Open space near streamsides is useful for deer management, preferably as a succession of glades at least 100 metres long, screened from each other by tree groups overlapping the streamside space.

Headwater streams on steep slopes tend to be straighter, more vertical and often parallel and evenly spaced. If open ground strips are left on either side of such streams, the result looks highly geometric and artificial in a wooded landscape, splitting the forest and disrupting unity. The mass of the forest should be brought right across these streams at selected points to create a unified and more natural landscape. By doing so on only a few short stretches of stream, there are unlikely to be any adverse effects on water quality or aquatic life.

Where streams cross the lower margin of the forest in steep country, the streamside space should be widened in asymmetrical bell-mouth fashion. This is particularly important where streams meet lake shores.

42. A well developed streamside with plenty of broadleaves and open space in Glamorgan.

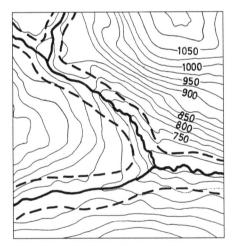

43a. Streamside design. The typical distances that planting is required to be kept clear of the stream.

b. Ploughing is designed to create a varied edge related to landform and avoiding run-off directly into the stream.

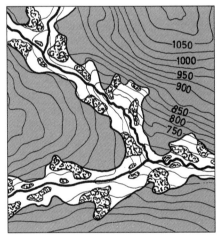

c. Planting of the conifer edge which comes closer to the stream in some places is kept further back in others. Broadleaves are used to develop the pattern of open space and dapple shade and to create good habitat in the corridor.

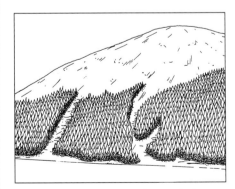

44a. Continuous open space along vertical headwater streams can create awkward shapes and breaks the unity of the forest.

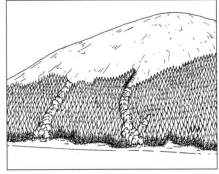

b. If the space becomes filled with self-sown broadleaves the impact is less but shape and unity are still inadequate.

c. The combinations of open space, broadleaved planting and some conifers close to the streams creates a more unified and diverse pattern.

Lakesides

Forests around lakes and reservoirs are particularly sensitive because of the quality of the flat reflective water surface. Continuous woodland around a lake tends to divide the lighter sky and water by a dark band. Open ground, with its intermediate colour and texture, can unite the landscape. An interlocking pattern of forest and open ground achieves the best effect.

The appearance of the natural line of the water tends to be lost when trees are planted close to the shore. This is most obvious where a promontory extends into the lake. Promontories are best kept as open space, allowing views across to water beyond. The forest should be brought to the water's edge at some points, other wise it will seems to float on a ribbon of open space. Groups of trees which overlap with the forest edge and which overhang the water help to create the necessary links between water and woodland.

Streams and lakesides are important for wildlife, and the needs of the latter have to be balanced with those of landscape. The ideal is to establish a broad pattern of woodland edges, the dense tree cover merging into scrub, then open space - which may well be wetland or waterside vegetation, thus giving a gradual change of vertical scale.

45. Tarn Hows, Cumbria. Interlocking open space and woodland in a unified composition with water and sky. The edges of the water and forest draw the eye to a focal point where an open space links water and sky.

Small Spaces

Smaller open spaces within the forest are a valuable source of diversity and are a particular consideration in planning picnic places, car parks and similar areas. These spaces should have edges which define the space without being claustrophobic. Proportions are important - dense edges of conifers can be very oppressive if the width of the space is less than 3 times tree height, especially in narrow valleys. A width of 10 times tree height loses the sense of enclosure altogether. Enclosed space within these limits makes a comfortable change and contrast with open ground.

Edges of internal spaces should draw the eye easily from one part of the space to another while emphasising any focal points. They should vary the width of the space, avoiding geometric or symmetric shapes.

Trees and shrubs judiciously placed within the space provide points of interest, can soften abrupt junctions of vertical wooded edge with the plane of the ground, and can add useful elements of diversity.

Open space around rocks and crags will depend on their size and importance as landscape features, and the steepness of the ground below. Leave sufficient space so that they are not obscured when trees are fully grown, designing the open space so created in the same manner as for other forest shapes.

46. The open ground below this crag allows it to be seen clearly in views from the right of this picture.

47. An interesting open space which helps diversify the forest. Here it has come about as a result of the presence of archaeological remains. The irregular shape and the presence of broadleaves complete the effect.

Views

Views are an important aspect of open space and viewpoints should be identified and incorporated in the woodland design. Trees in the foreground and middle ground should provide a setting for the view rather than competing with it.

Views take a variety of forms. Examples include:

- panoramic views, usually seen from high ground over steep slopes should have little fore or middle ground restriction. Any trees in the foreground should have a gently curving edge to underline the view; this is more effective than abrupt enframement;

- feature views are dominated by one or a few eye-catching elements. The woodland should draw the eye to them;

- focal views occur in valleys, with ridge lines directing the eye to the lower slopes. Overhanging trees can emphasise the point of convergence;

- canopied views utilise the trees as the overhead plane, and are best appreciated on foot. They can be developed by appropriate management, and possibilities for exploiting this device should be identified, particularly near recreation areas;

- filtered views are seen through an open screen of foreground trees. They must be used with caution, as the screen often closes up quickly and obscures the view. An open view is often preferable, particularly if a series of openings can be made alongside well used roads or paths.

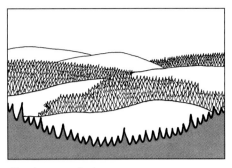

48a. A panoramic view.

b. A feature view.

c. A focal view.

d. A canopied view.

e. A filtered view.

LANDSCAPE AND FOREST OPERATIONS

Fences

A fence line is often visible mainly as a boundary between contrasting vegetation, caused by different grazing pressures. This looks artificial if the fence encloses geometric shapes particularly when these enclose areas outside the forest edge. It can sometimes be alleviated by running the fence on an irregular diagonal alignment so that the trees obscure the fence line as they grow up. This approach is worth pursuing when negotiating for the purchase or sale of land, but difficult to put into practice on existing ownership boundaries. An alternative in prominent face-on situations is to use selective herbicides to create irregular vegetation shapes or to erect non boundary fence lines.

Intrusive fence line effects can be reduced by:

- positioning fences where there is least impact, for example in hollows, away from skylines, close to the woodland edge;

- running fences diagonally to the contours, not following them or going straight uphill;

- making fences follow landform, going up in hollows and down on spurs;

- changing direction at irregular intervals, in scale with the landscape, and avoiding right angles;

- following the forest edge closely or else leaving an intervening shape or appropriate scale;

- using high-tensile spring steel fencing particularly along roadsides. This uses fewer posts and looks better than post and wire fences, as well as being cheaper.

Upland fence alignments should allow sheep or deer to move safely downhill to shelter in bad weather, without requiring them to go sharply uphill or to retrace their steps.

Lowland woodland fences have often to follow straight field boundaries, the harsh lines of which can be softened by shaping the planted area within the straight fences. The resulting areas of rough semi-natural vegetation on the unplanted ground form a most useful gradation from the field headlands to the edge of the trees.

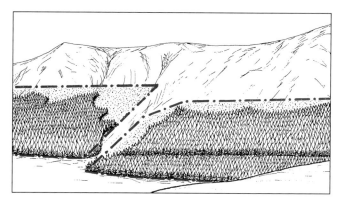

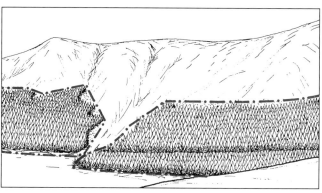

49a and b. Fence line adjustment at Ennerdale in Cumbria to avoid continuing geometric shapes after the forest has been redesigned.

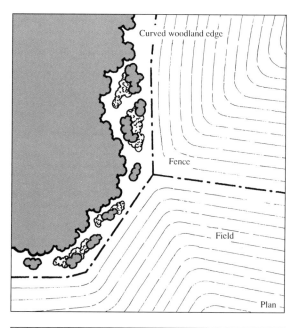

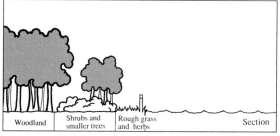

50. Fence alignment in lowland areas.

Cultivation and Drainage

Furrow ploughing for cultivation or drainage is often a major landscape change, often perceived to be environmentally intrusive. This is particularly so on gentle and even slopes. There is an obvious contrast between ploughed and unploughed ground, and the plough lines may be the dominant visual feature. Ploughing should be planned so that:

- unploughed areas such as steep slopes are irregularly shaped to follow land form, even if they will be hidden by trees eventually;

- unploughed access routes follow natural breaks in the slope and lower, less visible ground, and are kept to a minimum;

- furrows follow natural changes of slope in gentle curves, not at varying angles to the slope;

- ploughing direction is changed more frequently in smaller scale landscapes with close views. This is particularly important along public roadsides, where furrows running at the same angle to long stretches of road are monotonous.

Cultivation by rippers, scarifiers and mounders is normally much less obtrusive than ploughing.

The alignment and gradient of drains is determined by the need to remove water efficiently while avoiding erosion and sedimentation of natural watercourses. These requirements often result in satisfactory curving shapes. Avoid straight alignments, even on short cut-off drains on cultivation ploughing.

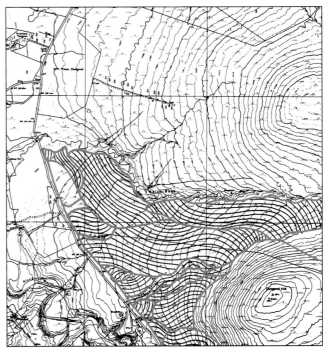

51a and b. A ploughing pattern at Whitelee Forest, Ayrshire, which responds to landform and reduces the impact of landscape change.

52. Mounding has been used instead of furrow ploughing on this site. While the overall impact is less, the eye can still pick up the straight alignments over some parts of the site and the rather straight edge along the stream.

The Choice of Species

The species pattern can reflect the broad pattern of the landscape, the pattern of ground vegetation, or the local landform which will become hidden beneath the tree canopy. It is best to follow whichever is the more dominant in the landscape.

In the initial planting of bare land, species layout should fit the shapes of well-designed external margins and open space. One species should appear to dominate the landscape composition by about two-thirds. Though contrasting species bring diversity, too much variety appears confusing. Different species mixed intimately disappear into an overall pattern or texture and need to be treated as a homogeneous element in forest design. An overlapping and interlocking pattern of a few contrasting species, in scale with the landscape, gives better overall unity.

The margins between species should be designed in the same way as other forest shapes. Mixing adjoining species at the boundary to make a 'soft' transition can be advantageous, but is no substitute for a well-designed shape.

The mixing of species at a common margin should be done by planting a few groups and individuals of one species within the mass of the other, or by extending groups and single trees of each into the other.

Broadleaves are often established with the aid of a conifer nurse. This is rarely essential except in exposed upland conditions and motives for doing so are usually economic.

53a. A poor species pattern of Taf Fechan, South Wales. The shape and scale of the larch and pine creates a very intrusive effect.

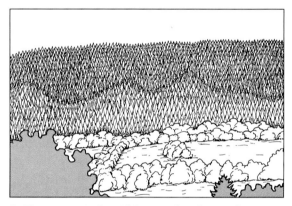

b. The same species but with better scale and more relation to landform.

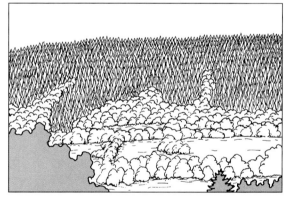

c. Broadleaves connect the pattern with that of the valley floor.

d. With less broadleaf the conifer comes down the valley floor in places increasing the interlock and unity of the design.

54. These broad bands of conifers are at least as intrusive as single rows. Felling the conifers will not remove the banded appearance.

55. In this example larch has been used in mixture with evergreen. Although the junction of the mixed area with the pine evergreen is blurred, the general rectangular shape remains prominent. The overall shape of the area to be planted with mixtures should have been designed to follow landform or vegetation pattern first.

56. This example shows some interesting variations on mixtures and merged margins. While the external margin and larch/fir belt are a problem, some of the more irregular areas of mixture with graduation in density are starting to offer possibilities. In some places the strong merging at junctions helps to soften the species transition very well.

Treeshelters

Planting trees in rigid translucent plastic tubes enables individual trees to be established quickly. Even when used with care, they appear very artificial, particularly in large numbers. Temporary fencing to exclude browsing animals and correct herbicide treatment to secure rapid early tree growth is cheaper and looks better on larger areas.

Shelters are best used to establish small groups and individual trees, and should:

- be of an unobtrusive colour, to blend with surroundings. Russet browns or olive greens are usually best. Avoid white or garish greens;

- be positioned in irregular fashion, not in geometric patterns;

- be well staked and securely erected. Leaning shelters give an impression of dereliction and incompetence.

Residual stakes and decayed plastic should be cleared away when the shelters are no longer required.

57a and b. White treeshelters stand out and look intrusive but olive green and brown in irregular groups blend into the landscape and reduce their impact.

Felling

Felling and replanting involve significant landscape change and provide an opportunity to improve shape, scale, diversity and unity. Felling plans should encompass the whole pattern of felling coupes, woodland margins, choice of restocking species, and the character, sensitivity and detail of the forest landscape. The design of felling should be taken forward over several decades, to ensure that work in the short term does not cause problems in the future - particularly important where the existing forest has a narrow spread of ages and where it is therefore desirable to increase the range of age classes.

The design of all felling should take account of the following:

- felling coupes should be designed for efficient harvesting and should not be isolated from road access by replanted areas or by unthinned retained stands;

- coupes should reflect the scale of the landscape, being smaller in valleys and lower slopes, larger on higher ground;

- coupes should be asymmetric and irregular, shaped to follow landform with edges diagonal to the contour, rising in hollows and descending on spurs;

- coupes should be comprehensively planned for the whole landscape composition. Timing of felling of adjacent coupes is vital and depends on the length of time that it takes for new planting or regeneration to close canopy, when difference of colour and texture become apparent.

Depending on site fertility, eight to fifteen years should elapse between the felling of adjacent coupes;

- skylines should be treated on a large scale, they should either be kept wooded or cleared sufficiently to reveal their true shape;

- eliminate intrusive straight lines and other geometric shapes of the previous crop, and do not reinstate them in replanting. This may require some cutting in adjacent immature stands;

- identify features previously hidden and now revealed by felling such as water bodies, crags and views from roads or recreation area. Design the replanting to enhance these;

- avoid felling areas which are too small or scattered; these create an unwelcome spotty appearance. Badly planned group felling can have the same result;

- scattered whippy and drawn-up trees should not be left standing on felled areas. Irregular groups of well formed trees especially when near the edge of the coupe may be worth retaining, but avoid continuous belts;

- windthrow risk may inhibit felling of irregular coupes. Windfirm features and edges should be included in the landscape design as far as possible but long straight internal edges should not be used even if they are windfirm. Felling should stop short at an irregular edge.

58a. At Coed Y Brenin in Wales felling has been going on for some time and has now come to be planned in a particularly sensitive area.

Visual forces pushing forest shapes down convex slopes

Visual forces pulling forest shapes up concave slopes

Straight ride / compartment boundaries

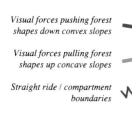

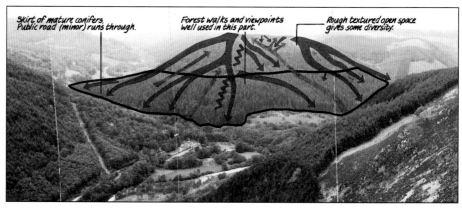

b. The visual appraisal. The convex landform predominates with a major concavity leading from the river valley up the focus of the view. An area of large Douglas fir is to be retained in the sheltered ground in the valley bottom.

Phase 1

Phase 1 (do not restock)

Phase 2

Phase 3

Phase 4

Long term retention

c. The felling is planned for the whole area with coupe shapes related to landform and the scale increasing from valley bottom to hill top. The felling will occur at 7-year intervals in order to ensure a high degree of diversity.

Sitka spruce

Japanese larch

Douglas fir

Broadleaves

d. When the felled areas are replanted larch will be used to highlight the convex landform and broadleaves used to connect the forest to the surrounding landscape.

e. The forest after the first phase is felled.

f. The forest after the last phase is felled and the previous phases have been replanted and are growing at different ages producing different textures.

59. At Ennerdale Forest in Cumbria an integrated, comprehensive plan has been in implementation for over 10 years. The pattern of coupes, their shape and the age differences are now showing up very well.

DESIGN ALONG ROADS AND FOOTPATHS

Woodlands beside roads, rides and footpaths should give an interesting sequence of views with a succession of varied spaces. A motorist cannot take in a wealth of detail so design of public road edges has to be on a broad scale and related to the average speed of the traffic.

- Keep landscape simple and undistracting at junctions, sharp bends, steep hills and blind summits. The driver's attention ought to be on the road.

- The woodland edge can be brought closer to the road on bends and steep hills, where the constricted space enhances the sense of movement. Edges should be further back on gentle alignments, with occasional features near the road.

- Existing edges which are straight, parallel to the road, equidistant on either side and strongly enclosing should be improved as soon as an opportunity arises, and more varied and interesting edges created.

- The sides of views opened through the woodland from public roads should be splayed out at acute angles. Narrow parallel sided openings at right angles to the road are often missed altogether by the motorist. To a lesser degree the same principle applies to rides and footpaths.

- Changes in landscape character, such as from open moorland to forest, can be emphasised by artificial features such as a massive gateway in the fence or wall, or by an archway created by the canopy of trees on either side.

60. On this bend a clearing has been made to open up a view to a river. The gap size is related to road speed.

61. A larger clearance is necessary to afford wider views out to more distant parts of the landscape.

62. The view here leads the eye over the forest to the mountain in the background. Management of the roadside will be needed to maintain the view but not to compete with it. Penningham Forest, Dumfries.

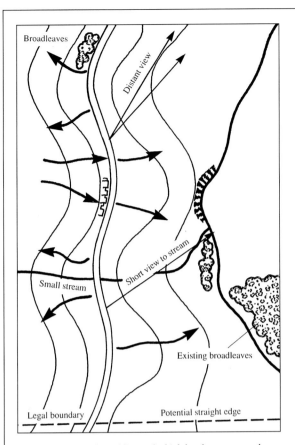

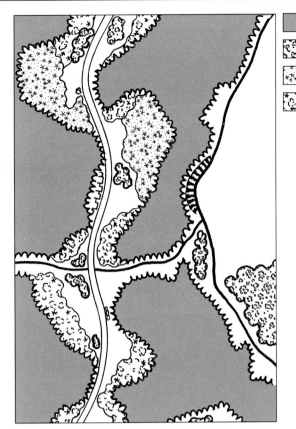

mature conifer forest

broadleaves

young conifers

thinned forest edge

63a. A diagram of a public road which has been surveyed to identify landform and landscape features of importance to the roadside design.

b. The design of the roadside spaces with varying widths related to landform, different ages, species and densities of trees being planted and views to natural features retained.

THE PROCESS OF FOREST LANDSCAPE DESIGN

Forest landscape design is about much more than creating visually pleasing results. The process through which a design is achieved involves integrating functional requirements, site constraints and opportunities and the costs involved.

The first stage of the process is the development of the brief. Here the designer and the client must agree on the objectives of the proposal and the limitations within which they are working. Under the Woodland Grant Scheme the owner's objectives must be set within the framework of the environmental considerations to be safeguarded.

The second stage is to survey the site and to obtain the necessary physical information such as contours, soils, windthrow hazard, information on ecology, archaeology, recreation and any forest already present in terms of species and ages. If felling is to be considered then information about harvesting systems, access for timber lorries and the desired felling ages of various stands is also needed. The survey should also include a visual assessment, checking out the visibility, sensitivity and character of the site in its wider context. All this should be recorded on maps together with photographs of the site.

The third stage of the process is to analyse the surveyed information. This stage is composed of two parts. Firstly the analysis of the site factors should determine those which constrain and those which provide opportunities for forest development, and by how much. Secondly the visual appraisal aims to identify the patterns which form the landscape as we see it - shapes, visual forces in landform, scale, existing elements of diversity, unifying factors and the spirit of the place. It should also identify existing and potential aesthetic problems.

These two aspects should be recorded on plan and in perspective.

At this stage, before any design actually begins, a decision must be taken as to whether or not tree planting is appropriate.

The fourth stage, design synthesis, is the most difficult. The objectives and site appraisal (survey and analysis) are brought together to enable a design concept to be prepared. This involves understanding how the landscape character and patterns work so that they can be followed as the major influences determining how a forest can best be fitted in. As detailed design proceeds each step of its development should be tested against the constraints and opportunities analysis. The various steps in the preparation of the actual design are as follows:

- deciding on the overall extent of the forest and the form of the external margin;

- defining: open space within the forest; shapes and timing of felling, where appropriate; species patterns and layout of broadleaves; detailed edge design; treatment of special sites.

The final design or design option should then be tested against the cost parameters.

The techniques to carry out the design stage include using panoramic photographs, either as photocopies or with transparent overlays to visualise the effect of the forest in the landscape. Computer aids are also available which enable designs to be tested accurately from different viewpoints and mapping to be checked.

REFERENCES

Bell, S., 1993

Elements of Visual Design in the Landscape.
E & F N Spon, London.

Forestry Commission, 1985

Guidelines for the Management of Broadleaved Woodland..
Forestry Commission, Edinburgh.

Forestry Commission, 1992

Lowland Landscape Design Guidelines.
HMSO, London.

Forestry Commission, 1991

Community Woodland Design Guidelines.
HMSO, London.

Forestry Commission, 1993

Forests and Water Guidelines (3rd Edition)
HMSO, London.

Forestry Commission, 1992

Forest Recreation Guidelines.
HMSO, London.

Hibberd, B.G. (ed.), 1991

Forestry Practice.
Forestry Commission Handbook 6. HMSO, London.

Lucas, O.W.R., 1991

The Design of Forest Landscapes.
Oxford University Press, Oxford.

Rackam, O., 1990

Trees and Woods in the British Landscape.
J M Dent, London.

Ratcliffe, P.R., 1985

Glades for Deer Control in Upland Forests.
Forestry Commission Leaflet 86. HMSO, London.